With special thanks to the SpongeBob SquarePants writers

Stephen Hillenburg

Based on the TV series *SpongeBob SquarePants*®
created by Stephen Hillenburg as seen on Nickelodeon®

ISBN 0-439-39086-9

12 11 10 9 8 7 6 5 4 3 2   2 3 4 5 6 7/0

Printed in Mexico

First Scholastic printing, February 2002

Life's a Beach

and Other

SpongeBob-isms

SCHOLASTIC INC.

New York Toronto London Auckland Sydney
Mexico City New Delhi Hong Kong Buenos Aires

Ahoy there, mates!
Ready to sing the
SpongeBob SquarePants
theme song?

I can't hear you!

Plenty of Fish in the Sea

SpongeBob on Relationships

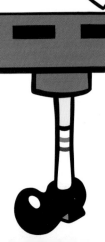

This is great,
Squidward! Just the
three of us. You, me ...
and this brick wall you
built between us.

This isn't just any ordinary ol' handshake! This is a *Friendly* handshake!

Winding up with no one
Is a lot less fun
Than a burn from the sun
Or sand in your buns.

Mollusks are People Too!

SpongeBob on Snail Care

You know what
they say, Gary,
"Curiosity salted the snail."
Mind your wandering eye,
you little mollusk.

You need to take Gary on a walk twice a day. His leash is in the closet. In the morning you've got to wax his shell and massage his eyes.

IF I close my eyes, it doesn't seem so dark.

SpongeBob ScaredyPants

SpongeBob on Fear

PATRICK: Sometimes we have to go deep inside ourselves to solve our problems.

SPONGEBOB: I'm scared.

PATRICK: Then I'm going in . . . for you!

Oh, Barnacles!
SpongeBob on Failure

> PATRICK: Where are we, SpongeBob?
> SPONGEBOB: Rock Bottom.

PATRICK: What's that smell?
SPONGEBOB: That, Patrick, is the smell of defeat.

Look at me . . . I'm naked!

SpongeBob on Vanity

SpongeBob FryCook

SpongeBob on Career

A Friend in Seaweed Is a Friend Indeed

SpongeBob on Friendship

No, you can't pop him! He's not just a bubble! He's a bubble buddy! He's my friend, and I love him!

As long as these pants are square
and this sponge is BOB,
I will not let you down!

Unsinkable!

SpongeBob on Self-Esteem

I am confident
in my abilities to
successfully succeed.

Now, I learned a lesson
I won't soon forget.
So listen up and
you won't regret.
Be true to yourself,
don't miss your chance,
And you won't
end up like the fool who
ripped his pants!

MuscleBob BuffPants

SpongeBob on Fitness

> I start out with twenty raw eggs every day, but that's just me.

The Art of Being SpongeBob

SpongeBob on Motivation

Don't give up, Patrick! This time I've got something I know you can do! We're going to . . . open a jar!

BE the net!

Don't be a stick in the sand.

Nautical Nonsense

SpongeBob on Life in Bikini Bottom

Oh, tartar sauce!
I'm **going** to a
different dream.

This really IS
your best day ever.

C'mon, crack of dawn! Start cracking!

Did I do something funny?

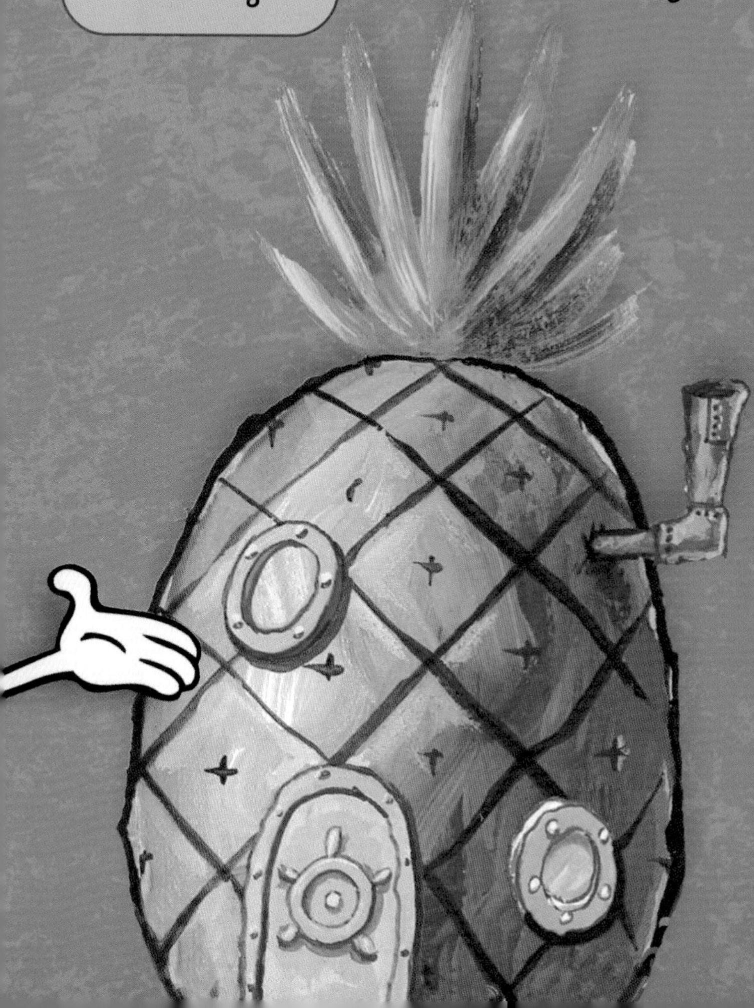